★ ★ ★ ★ ★ ★ ★ ★ ★ ★ ★ ★ ★ ★ ★ ★ ★ ★ ★ ★

WORLD'S MOST INCREDIBLE PUZZLES

CHARLES BARRY TOWNSEND

 Sterling Publishing Co., Inc. New York

This book is dedicated to the Maplewood Gang of Four: Stan, Gloria, Carey, and Lee Nemerowicz. We miss you all.

Library of Congress Cataloging-in-Publication Data

Townsend, Charles Barry.
　　World's most incredible puzzles / by Charles Barry Townsend.
　　　　p.　　cm.
　　Includes index.
　　ISBN 0-8069-0504-2
　　1. Puzzles—Juvenile literature.　　I. Title.
　GV1493.T6876　　　1994
　793.73—dc20　　　　　　　　　　　　　　　　93-39527
　　　　　　　　　　　　　　　　　　　　　　　　　　　CIP
　　　　　　　　　　　　　　　　　　　　　　　　　　　AC

10　9　8　7　6　5

First paperback edition published in 1995 by
Sterling Publishing Company, Inc.
387 Park Avenue South, New York, N.Y. 10016
© 1994 by Charles Barry Townsend
Distributed in Canada by Sterling Publishing
% Canadian Manda Group, One Atlantic Avenue, Suite 105
Toronto, Ontario, Canada M6K 3E7
Distributed in Great Britain and Europe by Cassell PLC
Villiers House, 41/47 Strand, London WC2N 5JE, England
Distributed in Australia by Capricorn Link (Australia) Pty Ltd.
P.O. Box 6651, Baulkham Hills, Business Centre, NSW 2153, Australia
Manufactured in the United States of America
All rights reserved

Sterling ISBN 0-8069-0504-2 Trade
　　　　　　0-8069-0505-0 Paper

Contents

Introduction

Are you ready for another helping of puzzles and problems? This is the eighth book in our series and I can promise you it's one of the best. You'll find the usual variety of material along with interesting and amusing illustrations. We've never categorized our puzzles according to type or difficulty. We don't have chapters dealing with coin puzzles, or math puzzles, or word puzzles. In fact, we don't have chapters at all. As you work your way through this book, we want you to be confronted with a different and exciting challenge on every page.

To illustrate our point, we have problems that deal with such subjects as cold fusion, schoolwork in a medieval castle, the weight of our local butcher, an escape from a prison ship, and a couple of mysteries from ancient Egypt. Calvin Collectible presents a puzzle dealing with antique toys, and a magician conjures up a problem employing coins and rabbits. We even have a spirit problem, a trolley ride, and a visit by the Masked Lady of Bayonne, who confounds one and all with a magic-square mystery. You'll go to court, play cards, and learn how the famous knife-and-egg wager is won.

Does this sound like fun? You bet it does, and these items are only the beginning. We're challenging you to solve 97 of the most incredible puzzles to be found anywhere! As the Chinese would say, "The longest puzzle book starts with the first problem!" So sharpen your pencils, settle back in your chair, and turn to that famous mystery, "The World's Most Incredible Dress Puzzle."

PUZZLES

World's Most Incredible "Dress" Puzzle

Mrs. White, Mrs. Black and Mrs. Grey were chatting in the garden. One was wearing a white dress, one a black dress and the third a grey dress. Mrs. Grey looked around and said, "We're all wearing dresses that are the same color as our names but none of us is wearing a dress that is the same color as her name!"

"What difference does that make?" asked the lady wearing the black dress.

With these sparse clues can you tell what color dress each of the three ladies had on?

World's Most Incredible "Number" Puzzle

"And then our substitute teacher, Ms. Sunshine, asked the class if anyone could think of a positive number that, when added to 1,000, would give a sum greater than multiplied by 1,000. Well, the answer just popped into my head and I got my first gold star for figuring it out! Shouldn't I get a reward?"

"All right, Winthrop, I'll take you to the soda shop, but only if you'll tell me the answer first!"

What an interesting problem! Come up with the answer in five minutes and you'll beat Winthrop to Pop Brady's Sip and Spoon Soda Emporium.

World's Most Incredible "Carpentry" Puzzle

That old cut-up, Hiram Ballpeene, had everyone stumped down at the lumberyard the other day. He brought in an irregular sheet of plywood and challenged the millworkers to cut it into three pieces that could then be reassembled to form the top of a two-foot-square table. Let's see if you can rip out the answer in jig time.

World's Most Incredible "Billionaire" Puzzle

The ballots are in and the rankings of the country's top seven billionaires are in. The above regal gentleman is obviously the winner. From top to bottom the standings are:

Henry has more money than Everett.

Sidney has more money than Winston and less than Waldo.

Alfred has as much money as Norbert, less than Waldo and more than Sidney.

Everett has more money than either Norbert or Waldo.

Each billionaire is worth, in even billions, from one to six billion dollars. Can you rank them for us, along with their individual worth?

World's Most Incredible "Tomb" Puzzle

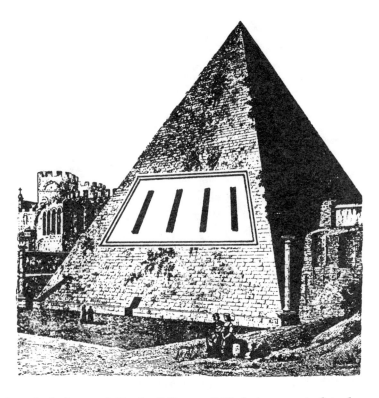

The slightly mad Earl of Cross Stitch is reputed to have died trying to solve a rather easy puzzle during a night of carousing. In an unguarded moment he bet his valet £1,000 he could solve any puzzle. Smedley challenged the earl to prove, using six matches, that four plus two equals nothing. The earl couldn't meet the challenge and died of apoplexy the next morning at the thought of his valet beating him out. His pyramidal tomb depicts the layout of the four matches that did the earl in. Can you add two matches to them and prove that four plus two does indeed equal nothing?

World's Most Incredible "Real Estate" Puzzle

Sidney, a local real estate maven, has boxed himself into a corner again. He bought an irregularly shaped piece of property he now wishes to subdivide into eight building sites all the same size and shape. Can you show him where he should lay out the property boundaries so he can start showing these choice lots to prospective customers?

World's Most Incredible "Automation" Puzzle

Back at the turn of the century Professor Pepper exhibited many new scientific inventions. One of the best liked by the public was the Little Clown Puzzle Generator pictured here. To activate it all you had to do was turn the crank at the base of the generator. The figure drew a different puzzle every time. In the above puzzle you were required to draw the figure using one continuous line. The line could not cross over itself at any point nor could you retrace any part already drawn. Let's see if you can do as well as the little clown!

World's Most Incredible "Match" Puzzle

Many years ago, when smoking was the sophisticated thing to do, everyone carried matches and knew at least half a dozen match puzzles or games. Pictured above are twelve matches arranged in a square. This square encloses an area of nine square units. The side of these units are the length of a match. Can you rearrange these twelve matches so that they enclose an area of four square units? None of the matches can, of course, overlap.

World's Most Incredible "Checkers" Puzzle

Just when Cy Corncrib thought he had Pop Bentley cornered Pop turned the tables and beat Cy out of another quarter. Pop was playing the white pieces and it was his move. The white pieces were moving up the board and the black pieces were moving down. How did Pop pull the rug out from under Cy?

World's Most Incredible "Quotation" Puzzle

No clowning around on this one! There's a famous quotation hidden in the above frame of letters. To read it find the correct letter to start with and go around the frame twice, reading every other letter as you go. Don't be in a rush trying to solve this puzzle!

World's Most Incredible "Find-the-Items" Puzzle

Here's an easy spelling test for you. In the above grid of twenty letters are hidden the names of twenty items found around the house. When spelling an item start at any letter and move one letter at a time horizontally, vertically or diagonally until a word is spelled. During the spelling of any one word you cannot enter any box more than one time. If you can find more than the twenty words that we give, then you're eligible for a double gold star.

World's Most Incredible "Walking" Puzzle

*"Barstow, you #***@@, ###& idiot **&&&@, #@&* nincompoop!!!"*

Great Great Aunt Hattie could make a sailor blush. Every Monday she went to see her banker in the city and came home on the 5:00 o'clock train. One day she told her husband, Barstow, that she would be back an hour earlier and to pick her up at the station. Barstow forgot and went to get her at the usual time. When Hattie arrived and found no one there she started walking home. Barstow met her on the road and took her back to the house, where they arrived twenty minutes earlier than usual. Since Barstow always drove at the same speed can you figure out how long Hattie was walking before he picked her up? Also, how did Barstow keep dry when it rained?

World's Most Incredible "Face" Puzzle

One of the most famous acrobatic teams of all time was the celebrated Shanghai Six. Here they are about to perform their record-breaking feat of standing six high on each other's shoulders. Before they take off, study this picture and count how many complete faces you see. Are there six, or five, or only one?

World's Most Incredible "Find-the-Place" Puzzle

Hidden in each of the exclamations above are the cities in which the action is taking place. See if you can find the locales.

World's Most Incredible "Archaeology" Puzzle

"We'll be in all the history books for this find, Petrie! The fabled Theban Tablet of Tiles has been unearthed at last!"

"Quite right, Hawkings! You are to be congratulated. Now let's solve the puzzle. According to the papyrus, 'To know perfection is to know the total number of squares, both great and small, in the Tablet of Tiles.'"

How many squares can the reader find?

World's Most Incredible "Acronym" Puzzle

"ETBTFC"

"HSTASTIITHATC"

"TBONTBTITQ"

"ARBAONWSAS"

"ORRWATR"

"AHAHMKFAH"

Shh! Professor Hammington, world-famous Shakespearean acronym expert, is performing. An acronym is a word made up of the initials of other words. In Hammington's case he is reciting famous Shakespearean lines in the form of acronyms. Try your hardest to untangle these problems .. and damn'd be him that first cries "Hold, enough!"

World's Most Incredible "Artist" Puzzle

The famous society portrait artist, Winslow Brushright, has a colorful problem for you to solve while waiting for your sitting. Below are a list of nine items to be defined. The first few letters of each of the definitions will spell a color. For example, the definition of a scoundrel would be *black*guard. Now it's your turn!

1. A puritanical person
2. A prison
3. A new cowboy
4. An old man
5. A nut
6. A disease
7. A drink
8. A goblin
9. A football tactic

World's Most Incredible "Toothpick" Puzzle

"Here's an interesting problem, Mayor Fairweather. I've arranged these 24 toothpicks so they form nine small squares. See if you can remove five of them so you'll be left with six small squares."

Susan is entertaining Mayor Fairweather at the puzzle club today. Tea, sandwiches, and toothpick puzzles seem to be the main items on the menu. There's always room for one more at these afternoon sessions, so why don't you pull up a chair and give the mayor some help? He usually comes in second in this type of contest.

World's Most Incredible "Riddle" Puzzle

In 1851 the Gold Rush was two years old, and little old San Francisco was getting its first riddle contest convention. The people in the above scene are practising for the opening night's competition.

World's Most Incredible "Math" Puzzle

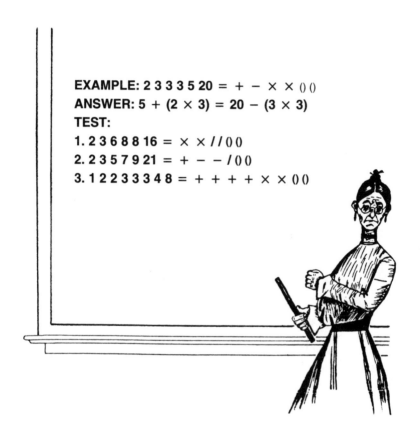

EXAMPLE: 2 3 3 3 5 20 = + − × × ( )
ANSWER: 5 + (2 × 3) = 20 − (3 × 3)
TEST:
1. 2 3 6 8 8 16 = × × / / ( )
2. 2 3 5 7 9 21 = + − − / ( )
3. 1 2 2 3 3 3 4 8 = + + + + × × ( )

Mr. Paterson has a cold today so your substitute teacher will be . . . Ms. Priscilla Sunshine.

"I've gotten reports that this class has become lax in the proper use of signs. Let's try a few problems to set you straight. I want you to make correct equations out of the numbers and signs given in each of the above three problems. Use each element only once per problem. While you're doing that I'll put another fifty problems on the board!"

World's Most Incredible "Treasure" Puzzle

Diver Duncan hit the jackpot the other day when he located the strong room in the wreck he was working on. The first four bags he brought up contained 60, 30, 20, and 15 gold coins, respectively. After he counted the coins in the remaining two bags he noted that the number of coins in each of the six bags corresponded to a specific progression. Knowing this, can you figure out how many coins were in bags five and six?

World's Most Incredible "Keyboard" Puzzle

"Well, Jenkins, you're certainly one of the best checkers players I've ever run into. You're into me for three dollars. How about a double-or-nothing wager? I'll bet you can't tell me what the longest common English word is that can be typed using the second row of letters from the bottom on a standard typewriter keyboard. In case you don't remember what those letters are, they're ASDFGHJKL. Care to take the bet?"

"You're on, Mr. Easymark. I was a typewriter repairman for 20 years and I know every blessed puzzle that's ever been devised using Mr. Remington's wonderful machine. The word you're looking for is _____ !"

World's Most Incredible "Medieval" Puzzle

Growing up in a castle wasn't all jousting and fighting. A certain amount of school work was also called for. Here we see Brother Venerable putting the lads through their paces with a substitute numbers problem. In this multiplication exercise certain of the figures have been replaced with asterisks. Let's see if you can put the problem back together again.

World's Most Incredible "Fusion" Puzzle

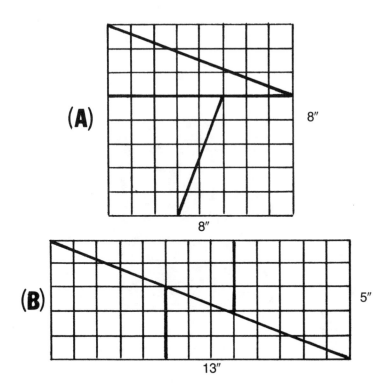

(A) 8″

8″

(B) 5″

13″

Here's a famous old puzzle that you can fool your friends with. Take a piece of stiff cardboard, cut it into a square 8 inches by 8 inches, and rule off 64 one-inch squares on it. Next, cut it into four pieces as indicated by the heavy lines. Now, when these pieces are assembled as shown in Figure A you have a square containing sixty-four smaller squares. If you then re-form them as shown in Figure B you will get a rectangle that contains sixty-five of these smaller squares. Where did the extra square come from? Could this be a case of cold fusion?

World's Most Incredible "Domino" Puzzle

Wilma the Witch has a devilish puzzle for you to figure out. This is one of the few puzzles you will come across dealing with dominoes. Remove the above eight dominoes from a box and lay them out in the form of a square, as depicted above. However, Wilma commands you to do it in such a way that the five numbers, along the four sides of the square, all add up to thirteen, Wilma's lucky number.

World's Most Incredible "Football" Puzzle

Professor Martin, Culpepper's all-around sports photographer, is shown here taking the picture of the four Kutlowski brothers, known as the Four Mules of Culpepper University. They were called the Four Mules because they stubbornly refused to wear any other number but nine on their jerseys. This in turn was the inspiration for the famous Kutlowski Nines Puzzle. The object of this puzzle is to arrange four nines so that their collective value equals 100. Can you come up with at least five different solutions to this problem and thereby make the goal?

World's Most Incredible "Find-the-Words" Puzzle

Now Showing

BSAINXLEATNTEARS

No, they're not having a Welsh film festival down at the Puzzle Theater, although you might think so by the name on the marquee. Buried within this string of sixteen letters are two words for you to find. To do this, merely remove six letters. The letters remaining will, without changing their order, spell out a word. You will have to do this twice to solve this tricky problem.

World's Most Incredible "Butcher" Puzzle

Herman Rumplemeir, our local butcher, has grown in stature and girth since coming to work here some 20 years ago. Some interesting facts concerning Herman are:

At age 20 his waist size was 92 cm and his weight was 77 kilo.

At age 30 his waist size was 96 cm and his weight was 82 kilo.

At age 35 his waist size was 104 cm and his weight was 93 kilo.

At age 40 his waist size is 114 cm. What does he weigh?

World's Most Incredible "Easy 'Z'" Puzzle

That Egyptian miracle worker, Joad Hereb, is about to perform his "Easy 'Z'" mystery. Before your very eyes he will cause this figure to split into three pieces which will then spin through the air and come back together again in the form of a perfect square. Can you determine where the cuts will be made and how the three pieces will be regrouped to form this square?

World's Most Incredible "Bloodhound" Puzzle

At the turn of the century the above dreary prison ship was anchored in the upper reaches of the East River. One night Knuckles Pommeroy swam ashore and headed for Long Island. Knuckles got a half-hour's start on his jailers. During the ensuing chase Knuckles was able to maintain a steady 3 miles per hour while the guards maintained 4 miles per hour. During the chase the warden's bloodhound raced forward until he caught up with Knuckles and then raced back to the guards. The dog went back and forth like this, all the time maintaining a steady 12 miles per hour, until Knuckles was apprehended. How far did the dog travel during the chase?

World's Most Incredible "Substitution" Puzzle

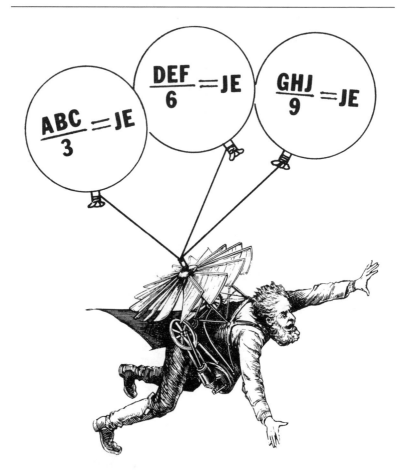

Here we have Ezra Flyright and his third-place entry in the 1903 Akron Balloon and Puzzle Competition. Each lighter-than-air contraption had to have a puzzle printed on its side. To solve Ezra's problem you are required to substitute numbers for the letters so the mathematical expressions are correct. The same number must be used for the same letter wherever it appears. Care to take a flyer on this one?

World's Most Incredible "Toy" Puzzle

Calvin Collectible hit the jackpot the other day when he came across a trove of old steel mechanical toys. Included were dump trucks, steam shovels and farm tractors. Let's make a puzzle of his find. He bought the following four lots of toys:

> The first lot had one tractor, 3 shovels and 7 trucks and sold for $140.
>
> The second lot had 1 tractor, 4 shovels and 10 trucks and sold for $170.
>
> The third lot had 10 tractors, 15 shovels and 25 trucks.
>
> The fourth lot had 1 tractor, 1 shovel and 1 truck.

The problem is to figure out how much Calvin paid for lots number three and four.

World's Most Incredible "Magic Coins" Puzzle

The man of mystery has laid out six magic coins. The first three are tails up and the last three are rabbit up. In three moves you are to change the order to tails, rabbit tails, rabbit, tails, rabbit. In each move you must turn over two adjacent coins.

World's Most Incredible "Rectangle" Puzzle

World's Most Incredible "Chicken" Puzzle

Chickens must be about the smartest of the barnyard animals, judging by the number of times they appear in puzzles. The other day Cy Corncrib, after losing another game of checkers to Pop Bentley, asked him the following question: If a chicken and a half lays an egg and a half in a day and a half, how many eggs can 6 chickens lay in 6 days? Pop is still working on that one. How many eggs do you think these chickens can lay?

World's Most Incredible "Alice" Puzzle

"So you're lost again, Alice. Well, I'll be happy to tell you how to get out of this garden but first you must answer this question. What do the following five words have in common? Brandy, pirated, swingers, tramps and grangers. I'll give you a hint—like you, they start off tall but end up small."

World's Most Incredible "Weight" Puzzle

"Right, sir! I'll tell Mr. Hackenbush as soon as he comes in. The total weight of boxes 1 and 2 is 12 pounds. Boxes 2 and 3 weigh 13½ pounds, boxes 3 and 4 total 11½ pounds, and boxes 4 and 5 total 8 pounds. Also, boxes 1, 3 and 5 total 16 pounds. You want him to figure out what each box weighs and to call you back right away. Have no fear, sir! I've got all the details right here in my head!"

I'd love to hear what Bascomb will remember when Mr. Hackenbush arrives. In the meantime, can you figure out what each box weighs?

World's Most Incredible "Spirit" Puzzle

DAESTU

THE WONDROUS WRITING POWER

"DAESTU" commends itself to intelligent and scientific minds and is destined to electrify the civilized world.

It is the ultimate development and perfection of other devices, having for their object the demonstration of the theory that thought can be transmitted by means of an involuntary medium.

$$TWO \times TWO = THREE$$

In exasperation these Victorian puzzle solvers have turned to the wondrous writing power of Daestu (sounds like a Japanese car). This distant relative of the Ouija board could apparently deliver the goods. The problem they are stuck on requires them to replace each letter in the above mathematical expression with a number so that two times two really does equal three. The same number must be used for the same letter wherever it appears.

World's Most Incredible "Trolley Ride" Puzzle

PALACE of FUN
25 AMUSEMENTS
UNDER ONE ROOF

Once a month Maynard took Emmeline to Olympic Park for an afternoon of fun and games. Unfortunately, Maynard never had enough money for two round-trip fares on the trolley so they always had to walk back. The round trip always took them eight hours. The trolley went at a speed of nine miles an hour and they could walk at a rate of three miles an hour. With these facts can you determine the total number of miles they travelled on these dates?

World's Most Incredible "Numero Uno" Puzzle

"To commemorate our great victory over the Spanish Armada, which, if you'll excuse the expression, made me Numero Uno in Europe, I've composed the following official puzzle: Create two numbers composed only of ones, which, when added or multiplied together, will give the same result. I pray that none of you will lose your heads trying to solve this one."

World's Most Incredible "Printing" Puzzle

Philo Ramsgate has gone into the printing business and his first customer has ordered 10,000 calendars from him. However, the customer insists that the names of the months be printed in an exotic three-dimensional type-face that will cost Philo a bundle. Each letter costs $5.00. What are the fewest number of letters Philo will have to buy in order to print, in full, the twelve months of the year?

World's Most Incredible "Musical Toys" Puzzle

When Papa Schoenberg died, he left his musical-toy manufacturing business to his three sons. The inventory of toys on hand was split up as follows: Alfred received 20 percent more toys than Julian, and 25 percent more than Cedric. Julian received 3,600 toys. Can you figure out how many toys Cedric received? After the boys sold the stock they converted the business over to making high-tech guitars for rock groups.

World's Most Incredible "Addition" Puzzle

```
  111
  333
  555
  777
  999
 ─────
2,775
```

Here we see Charlie Chin, the famous juggling puzzler, about to solve an addition problem submitted by a member of the audience. Charlie has to cross out six digits in the above five three-digit numbers so that when they are once again added together the total will be 1,111. (When a digit is crossed out consider that it is replaced by a zero.) Charlie will solve it in 30 seconds. Can you?

World's Most Incredible "Square" Puzzle

> "Razzmatazz! I think I've got it! I'll have my picture on the cover of Drafting Digest!"

It looks as though Waldo Quiller has solved the famous Lines and Squares puzzle. The object is to draw a figure with exactly 100 squares in it with the *fewest number* of straight lines. In the above example you'll find 20 squares. Twelve are one unit, six are four units, and two are nine units. Solve this one and you'll be up for Square-of-the-Month.

World's Most Incredible "Masked Lady" Puzzle

X	15	X	5
17	X	11	X
X	X	X	X
14	9	X	X

Back in 1897 the puzzle world was turned upside down when the Grand Puzzle Prize was won by the famous Masked Lady of Bayonne, New Jersey. She topped everyone by completing the above Magic Square in 54 seconds flat. To solve it, replace the X's in the grid with the correct numbers to create a square that adds up to 50 in each column, row, and on the two major diagonals. Use numbers 5 through 20; no number may be used more than once.

World's Most Incredible "Witch" Puzzle

One Halloween night a hapless, slightly tipsy farmer was captured by a malevolent witch who took him to a crumbling old church. "You are allowed to make one statement to save yourself!," she crooned. "If it is true I will boil you in oil. If it is false I'll feed you to my bats!" The farmer's befuddled brain cleared in an instant and he made a statement that caused the witch to curse him and set him free. What did the farmer say?

World's Most Incredible "Suitcase" Puzzle

Once upon a time the Hollywood Trunk and Suitcase Company ran a contest with the first prize an all-expenses-paid one-week trip to Tinseltown. All you had to do to win was divide the outline of a rather unusual suitcase into four parts. All the parts had to be the same shape and size. However, the shape could *not* be the same shape as the original suitcase. Let's see if you would have made it to the Land of Eternal Youth!

World's Most Incredible "Scales" Puzzle

WEIGHING ~THE~ BABY BY SAM LOYD

Here's a great old problem from the turn of the century by America's greatest puzzle creator, Sam Loyd.

"Mrs. O'Toole, being of an economical turn of mind, is trying to weigh herself, her baby, and her dog for one cent. If she weighs a hundred pounds more than the combined weights of dog and baby, and if the dog weighs sixty percent less than the baby, can you determine how much the little cherub weighs?"

World's Most Incredible "Counterfeit Coin" Puzzle

During the Crusades an English knight was captured and brought before the mighty Saladin. He was informed that he and his horse could go free if he paid a ransom of 100,000 pieces of gold.

"Great Saladin," spoke the knight, "I labor here at a disadvantage. In my country a prisoner is given a chance to do battle with his wits when he is captured. If he can correctly answer a puzzle put to him by his captors he is allowed to go free. If he fails the ransom is doubled!"

"So be it then," replied Saladin. "Here is your question: You are given twelve gold coins and a simple balance scale. One of the coins is counterfeit, but it is not known whether it is lighter or heavier than the other coins. You must find it, using only three weighings with the scale. You have until morning to solve this problem!"

So does the reader.

World's Most Incredible "What" Puzzles

"What's the difference between a gardener and a billiard player?"

"What is the noblest musical instrument?"

"What increases its value one half when turned upside down?"

"What trade have all the presidents of the United States been members of?"

"What motive led to the invention of railroads?"

The Watt family can't seem to say goodbye without launching into a round of "What" riddles. Care to play?

World's Most Incredible "Shakspearian" Puzzle

Hidden in the above wheel of letters are the names of three famous plays by the Bard of Avon. To find the plays, start at any letter and proceed clockwise reading every third letter. Nothing could be easier. As it is written in *Julius Caesar*,

> "There is a tide in the affairs of puzzlers,
> Which, taken at the flood, leads to swift solutions."

The curtain is up and you are center stage!

World's Most Incredible "Abe Lincoln" Puzzle

"All right, gentlemen, I feel lucky tonight. Who wants a piece of the action? Here's a brand-new five-dollar bill. I'll let anyone hold this bill above his head and then release it so it floats down to the floor. If it lands with Abe Lincoln's face up you'll pay me $5.00. If it doesn't I'll pay you $10.00. Who'll take my bet?"

J. Wellington Moneybags is back in town and up to his old tricks. It's best to steer clear of this wager since Wellington only bets on sure things. However, it would be nice to know how he intends to fleece his flock. Can you figure it out?

World's Most Incredible "Card Square" Puzzle

You'll need more than an ace up your sleeve to solve this one. First, remove all the face cards from the deck and put them aside. Next, remove nine cards, ace through nine, from the remaining deck and lay out the above magic card square. All the horizontal and vertical rows plus the major diagonals add up to 15. Your problem is to construct three more squares like the one above with the remaining cards in the deck. Each of these new squares must add up to a different sum. When you're finished you will have four cards left over. You have 30 minutes to ace this one.

World's Most Incredible "Scholar" Puzzle

First Scholar: "Confound it, Mossback, I can't find any word in the dictionary that contains three double letters in a row. It's maddening!"

Second Scholar: "Quite right, Ploddington. I've found plenty of words with two double letters in a row, like balloon or woolly, but none with three!"

First Scholar: "The club's accountant, Paul Pinchpenny, assures me that there is such a word but he won't tell me what it is. I think he should be fired!"

(There's a clue to the answer in the above conversation.)

World's Most Incredible "Punctuation" Puzzle

"Quimby, you've messed up again! I'm going to have to send you back to editing school. In this sentence from Alice Flutterheart's new book, "Passion Under the Banyan Tree," you've left out all of the punctuation!"

Melicent while Fabian had had had had had had had had had had had a better effect on the teacher.

Quimby's in hot water again. Above is the quotation his boss is talking about. Can you help him, with the addition of a few quotation marks, a couple of commas and a period, clean this mess up in time to get the manuscript out to the printer?

World's Most Incredible "Route" Puzzle

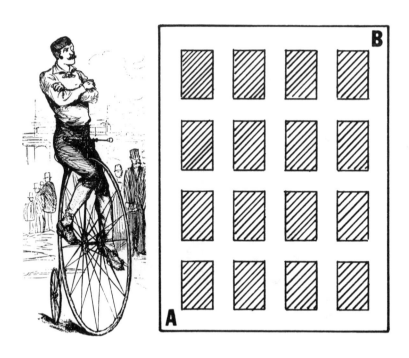

America has always had a warm spot in its heart for the gifted eccentric. Otto Von Sprocket, pictured above, is a prime example. During the Golden Age of Bicycling Otto was the chief engineer at the High Flyer Bike Works. Every morning Otto would leave his home at point **A** on our map and proceed to the bike works at point **B**. Otto liked to vary his journey by going a different route each day. Can you figure out how many different routes there are between his home and the plant? He always travelled upwards and to the right.

World's Most Incredible "Guru" Puzzle

"Listen closely, O unenlightened one:
'To know is to know.
Not to know is not to know.
A half is a third of it.'
Now go. I am very tired."

The old boy is really floating tonight. But that third pearl of wisdom is a tough one. What did he mean when he said "A half is a third of it"?

World's Most Incredible "Sears Hat" Puzzle

"Well, pardner, back where I come from if the range boss don't wear a Sears Texan Chief hat he don't get no respect!"

No. 33R2352 Texan Chief Cowboys' High Crown Mexican Style Sombrero Hat, 5-inch brim and 6¼-inch crown; fine leather sweatband; 1-inch silk ribbon band or tassel cord braided band, if desired. Flat, never flop brim with raw edge. One of the very best as well as the most popular sombreros ever made from best quality clear nutria fur. Full of real goodness and will give excellent satisfaction. Color, belly nutria. Sizes, 6¾ to 7¼. Price, each......**$4.25**
Price, without **fancy cord band**...............

Shades of Rodney Dangerfield! That sure is a handsome hat Sears sold back in 1902. However, in the ad the typesetter left out the price of the hat without the fancy cord band. Now, if the hat alone cost $3.75 more than the fancy cord band, how much would the fancy cord cost and how much would the hat cost without the cord?

World's Most Incredible "Bridge" Puzzle

The three men pictured above are named Claude, Horace, and Selwyn and they are married to the three ladies whose names are Deirdre, Erika, and Imogene, though not necessarily in that order. They are all enjoying a night out at the club. Let's see if you can guess who is married to whom.

Claude's wife and Erika's husband are bridge partners and they are playing Deirdre and Imogene's husband. None of the men are partners with their own wives. Finally, Horace doesn't play cards at all.

World's Most Incredible "Superstition" Puzzle

"The night is dark with bats in the air.
Unlucky numbers may give you a scare!
Hee, Hee, Hee!"

This is a good puzzle for those who are superstitious around Halloween time. Mr. Pumpkin has given you thirteen threes to work with. Arrange these numbers to form an equation equal to 100. You have until the harvest moon is full.

World's Most Incredible "Brick" Puzzle

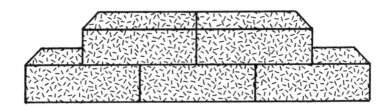

Quick Stack McGee, the star bricklayer of Branigan's Masonry Creations, is back with another of his Mortar Mysteries. On his last job Quick Stack placed five bricks on the ground and bet the other workers that they couldn't pick them all up at once with only one hand. And to make it harder he stipulated that the bricks couldn't be leaned against anyone's arm while being lifted. How did Stacks stump his compadres?

World's Most Incredible "Knife and Egg" Puzzle

"This puzzle should appeal to an egghead like you, Llewellyn!"

Carmela has a rather neat problem for Llewellyn to solve. After placing half an empty egg shell over the point of a table knife she rapped the end of the handle of the knife sharply against the top of the table causing the knife to penetrate through the top of the shell. Llewellyn spent the next 30 minutes trying to duplicate her feat without success. How do you think Carmela performed this eggstraordinary feat?

World's Most Incredible "Birthday" Puzzle

"What good is fame? What good are riches when the sands of time are running out? Two days ago I was fifty-four years old. Next year I shall be fifty-seven. What does it all mean anyway?"

Mr. Gotrocks is momentarily suffering from an attack of existential Angst. I'm sure it will quickly pass. However, from the clues in his statement can you figure out when his birthday is?

World's Most Incredible "Tree" Puzzle

The Deforester Brothers are this state's best tree surgeons. They've saved more of our state's forests than all our senators put together. A list of all the types of trees they've worked on is contained in the above puzzle. To find each tree start at any letter and move one square at a time in any direction. Do not use any square more than once for any given name. Do not skip over any letters. All the letters must be adjacent. You can move horizontally, vertically, or diagonally. There are at least seventeen trees in the diagram.

World's Most Incredible "Radio" Puzzle

"It's time to play 'Name Those Letters!' All our questions can be answered by using one or more letters of the alphabet. We'll give you the answer to the first question and then you're on your own!"

1. *Name of a beverage.* T (tea)
2. *Name of jealousy.*
3. *Name of a place in England.*
4. *Name of too much of something.*
5. *Name of a composition.*
6. *Name of a tent.*
7. *Name of an image.*
8. *Name of a badly dressed person.*
9. *Name of something void.*
10. *Name of part of a house.*
11. *Name of a foe.*
12. *Name of a sad poem.*

The questions from an early quiz program are coming through loud and clear on this beautiful old Lyradion radio. Each correct answer was worth a dollar. Let's see how much you would have made.

World's Most Incredible "Doggie" Puzzle

"Something you'll find in church!"

"July 3rd through August 11th!"

"The chief magistrate of Venice!"

"A comic verse, sometimes rude and crude!"

"A two-hour duty tour at sea!"

"Something found on a golf course!"

Every dog has his day, or in this case, his puzzle. Each one of the short clues presented by our canine friends refers to a word, or name, that starts with the letters *D-O-G*. Anything less than five right will land you right in the doghouse.

World's Most Incredible "Mind Reading" Puzzle

"All right, Madame Zorrina, the next test is extremely hard. This gentleman is thinking of a unique number. When spelled out, the letters in the number are in alphabetical order. The number is between one and one thousand. I must have absolute silence from the audience, please!"

"The gentleman has very powerful brain waves! Yes, I see a number forming through the clouds of skepticism emanating from those around him! Wait, the mists are clearing! The number is . . . !"

In all of her years on the vaudeville circuit Madame Zorrina never failed to deliver the goods. Let's see if you're as good at snatching messages from the ether as she was. Close your eyes, lean back in your chair and see if you too can see the number that the gentleman in the audience is thinking of.

World's Most Incredible "Indian" Puzzle

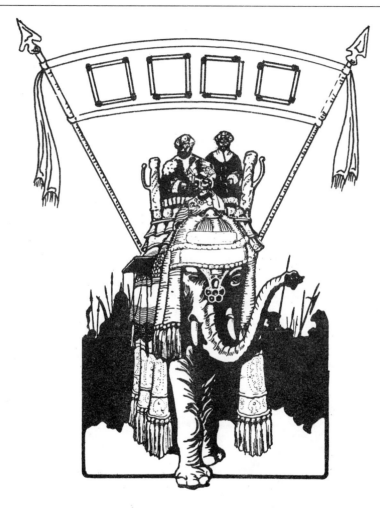

Shown here is the Puzzling Pooh Bah of Punjab making his entrance into last year's Puzzle Convention. His entry is pictured on the banner. First, lay out 16 matches in the form of 4 squares. Next, remove 4 matches and shift 3 others so that you have the answer to the question "What are matches made of?"

World's Most Incredible "Typewriter" Puzzle

1. T
    A
    L
    E
    S

2.   L
      EMOC
      2ME

3. xxEE
    mariage XXee

4. c To be or
       not to be c

5. EDalienEN

6. ECNALG

7. W A T E R

Each of the *doodle words* printed by the above typewriter represents a proper name, saying, or familiar object. The first doodle stands for "tall tales." Now, let's see if you can get the rest.

World's Most Incredible "Sharpshooter" Puzzle

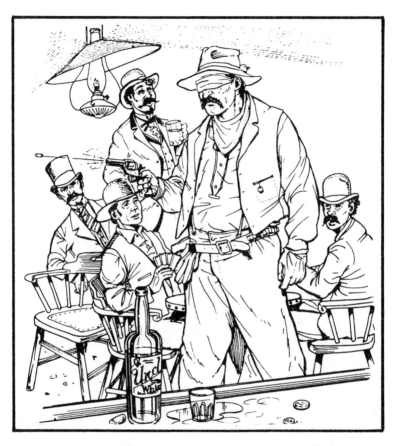

Pictured here is Big Nose George Parrott performing his famous Shoot the Easterner's Hat trick. George would hang the dude's hat up, put on a blindfold, walk down to the other end of the room and then turn around and shoot a hole through the crown of the hat. Big Nose won dozens of bets with this trick shot. Can you figure out how he did it? Remember, the blindfold was perfectly genuine and he never used more than one shot when ventilating the derbies.

World's Most Incredible "Prohibition" Puzzle

During Prohibition Swifty O'Brian was the fastest booze runner on Chicago's North Side. Here we see Swifty delivering twenty cases of Big Benny's finest hooch to four of his select clients. The drops went like this:

> Hanratty's received two more cases than the Dutchman's Cafe.
> Edna's Hide-a-Way received six less cases than Sal's Saloon.
> Sal's Saloon received two more cases than Hanratty's.
> The Dutchman's Cafe received two more cases than Edna's Hide-a-Way.

How many cases did each of these watering holes receive?

World's Most Incredible "Beheading" Puzzle

No, no, no, Sedgewick! Cut off the first letter of the word, not your own head. When you play the Beheading Game you chop off the first letter of a word in order to form another word. For example, behead a word meaning "not fast" and be left with a word meaning "not high." The word you are looking for is "slow." Now, try to find the following words.

1. Behead an animal and leave an animal.
2. Behead a vessel and leave a vessel.
3. Behead hard work and leave something slippery.
4. Behead a drill and leave a rock.
5. Behead a tool and leave a small road.
6. Behead a musical instrument and leave a musical instrument.
7. Behead what a debt does and leave a boating exercise.

World's Most Incredible "Change-the-Word" Puzzle

In Change-the-Word puzzles you must change the top word into the bottom word by changing one letter at a time as you go down the ladder. Each change must produce a new word. Try your hand at the following changes.

1. *WARM* to *COLD*
2. *MORE* to *LESS*
3. *FISH* to *MEAT*
4. *RIVER* to *WATER*
5. *WORK* to *EARN*

World's Most Incredible "Halloween" Puzzle

When I heard that the fun-loving Armbruster clan was getting together for a Halloween party I figured that they would have to hire a hall. Arlo told me that the party would consist of two grandfathers, two grandmothers, three fathers, three mothers, three sons, three daughters, two mothers-in-law, two fathers-in-law, one son-in-law, one daughter-in-law, two brothers and two sisters. He said no, the party would be at his house since the whole family consisted of just 10 people. Can you figure out how this is possible?

World's Most Incredible "Santa Claus" Puzzle

Even the animal helpers in Santa's workshop get time off for a pep rally as the great day draws near. Here they're working on a tricky math problem. To solve it you must substitute the numbers 1 through 9 for the nine different letters used in the math expression. You must end up with a correct subtraction problem. The same number is given to each occurrence of the same letter.

World's Most Incredible "Subtraction" Puzzle

Great Victorian Puzzles   Page 432

"The puzzler is required to subtract 45 from 45 in such a manner that there shall be 45 left." What an extraordinary problem. I'm sure that this must be a misprint!

Aunt Hattie looks the picture of Victorian comfort using her new Holloway Reading Stand that Grandpa gave her for Christmas. Propped on the book-rest is a copy of Professor Hoffmann's 1890s masterpiece, *Puzzles Old and New*. What do you make of the professor's interesting problem in subtraction?

World's Most Incredible "Airmail" Puzzle

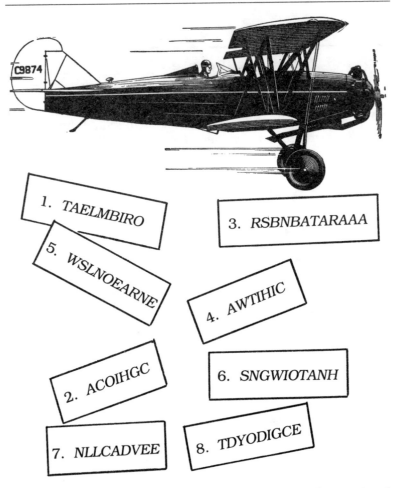

1. TAELMBIRO

3. RSBNBATARAAA

5. WSLNOEARNE

4. AWTIHIC

2. ACOIHGC

6. SNGWIOTANH

7. NLLCADVEE

8. TDYODIGCE

During the Roaring Twenties carrying the mail sustained the fledgling airplane industry in the United States. One of the bravest of these early fliers was Wing Walker. In one 72-hour period Wing visited the above eight cities. We've scrambled the letters of each city on the envelopes. Let's see if you can unscramble them before you run out of gas and crash-land in the answer section.

World's Most Incredible "Computer" Puzzle

"Well, Professor Henri, I certainly hope that your new computer can help me out. My students think me out of step because I can't seem to solve what they consider to be an absurdly simple problem. They challenged me to find the smallest number that when divided by 2, 3, 4, 5, or 6 will always leave a remainder of 1, and, when divided by 7, will leave no remainder at all. Can you help me?"

"But certainly, mon ami! I merely have to enter in the parameters of your little problem and voilà, out prints the answer! Here it is now! The number is . . . !"

World's Most Incredible "Piggy" Puzzle

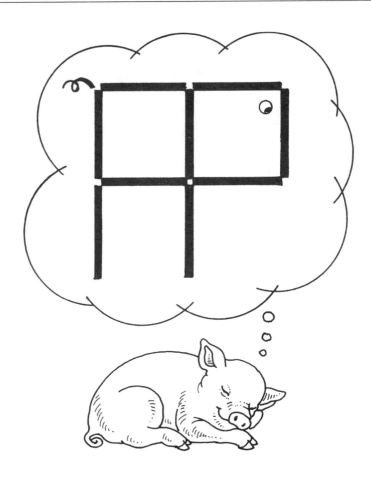

Pictured here is the lucky pig that didn't go to market. He stayed home and dreamt of the winning animal puzzle at last year's county fair. In the puzzle nine sticks were arranged in the shape of a pig. The problem was to move two of the sticks to new positions so that you would have three squares of equal size. Let's see if you can link up with the correct answer.

World's Most Incredible "Word" Puzzle

"Fool, this is your last chance. If you don't give me the answer to that puzzle you will no longer have a head for figures. For the last time, what are those two eight-letter English words that each contain the first six letters of the alphabet? One, two . . . !"

"I'd rather be in Philadelphia than give you the answers. However, I'll give you two hints. One of the words has to do with printing and the other word pertains to survey information. Now, how about a last cigarette? I know that they haven't been invented yet, but I can wait!"

World's Most Incredible "Sawing" Puzzle

THE GIANT RIDING SAW MACHINE.

This Wonderful Improved
SAW MACHINE

is warranted to saw a **2-foot log in three minutes**, and **more** cord wood or logs of any size in a day than **two men** can chop or saw the old way. Every Farmer and Lumberman needs one.

Cy Corncrib likes to tell the story about a puzzle that his grandfather, Ebenezer Corncrib, used to stump his fellow farmers with. One day Ebenezer saw an ad for a wonderful new sawing machine that would do the work of two men. He ordered one from the Farmers Manufacturing Company and used it for many years. Here's his puzzle. He took a finished wooden beam that weighed exactly 180 lbs. and cut it into eight pieces that each weighed exactly the same amount. How much did each piece weigh? A word of caution. Ebenezer was a tricky old bird.

World's Most Incredible "Beer" Puzzle

"Oh, Brunhilda, life is so wonderful. Just imagine, before I met you it used to take me 20 days to drink a barrel of beer!"

"I know, Otto my love. But now with me at your elbow the two of us can polish off that same barrel in only 14 days. Life is good!"

Obviously a marriage made in Bavaria. However, an interesting question arises from the above bit of conversation. If Otto wasn't by her elbow at all times, how long would it take Brunhilda to drink a barrel of beer all by herself?

World's Most Incredible "Pyramid" Puzzle

The above artist is going to be in a peck of trouble. The five-pointed star he painted depicts five straight roads and ten pyramids. Each road has four pyramids on it. Each pyramid can be directly approached from the desert. What the pharoah wanted was a design using five straight roads with four pyramids on each, but with two of these pyramids located within the design, so anyone coming in from the desert would have to cross one of the outer roads to get to them. What design should he use to keep from being sealed up when the tomb is closed?

World's Most Incredible "Movie Musical" Puzzle

During the filming of the 1937 musical *High Hat Hilarities*, the director, Buzzy Embarcadero, insisted on stacking four pianos four-high in a sixteen-cell grid. He also insisted that only one piano could appear in any row or column. Can you figure out how many different ways this could be done? Mirror images of any arrangement are not to be counted. (A mirror image of the above arrangement would go from the top right-hand corner to the bottom left-hand corner. Also, mirror images caused by giving the board a quarter turn left or right are not to be counted.)

World's Most Incredible "Stamp" Puzzle

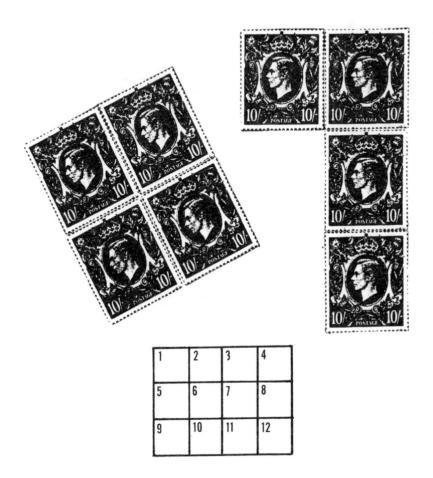

1	2	3	4
5	6	7	8
9	10	11	12

An English stamp collector had a sheet of 12 stamps, as pictured above. When a fellow collector asked to buy four, he specified that the stamps must be joined together along their sides. Can you figure out how many different ways the collector could tear them loose from the sheet above? Three possibilities are 1-2-3-4 or 5-6-7-8, and 7-8-11-12. Hint: there are over 50 possibilities.

World's Most Incredible "Geometry" Puzzle

The gentleman above is trying to discover the smallest number of squares the above drawing can be cut into. Cutting along all the lines yields 169 squares, the greatest number. For example, one square might be six by six (36 small squares), another four by four (16 small squares), and a third two by two (4 small squares). More than one square can be the same size, but they can't all be the same size. *Hint:* our solution has less than 20 squares of varying sizes.

World's Most Incredible "Baseball" Puzzle

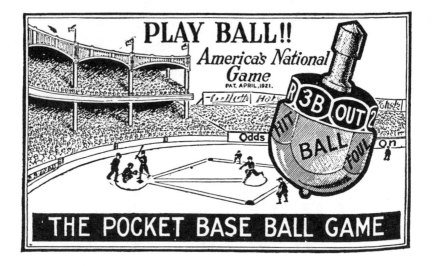

The above popular game from my youth puts me in mind of an interesting old puzzle dealing with the temperaments of the Gashouse Nine baseball team. When they were on the road the starting nine players liked to play hearts. They would set up three tables with three players at each table. However, no outfielder would play another outfielder at the same table, no baseman another baseman; and the shortstop, pitcher and catcher all refused to sit at the same table. In order to keep everyone happy, how many different three-table setups are needed before starting over?

World's Most Incredible "Poker Chip" Puzzle

Back in the 1920s a delightful line of books provided an endless source of cheap entertainment. For only ten cents a copy you could learn all about magic, puzzles, chess and boxing. Here's an interesting puzzle from one of these books.

On a large sheet of paper draw the above ten-box diagram. Place four white poker chips and four red poker chips on squares one through eight. Alternate the colors as shown. Now, moving two adjacent chips at a time to any two empty squares, change the order of the chips to that shown below. You must do this in only four moves.

World's Most Incredible "Sugar" Puzzle

It's tea time down at the local puzzle club. Mr. Okito is fuelling up for the above tough challenge from Juanita Witt. If Mr. Okito were from Texas instead of Japan he would have a better chance of solving it. That's a hint! Anyhow, join in the fun and try to come up with the answer before the last cucumber sandwich is gobbled up.

World's Most Incredible "Betting" Puzzle

"When the deck is cold, and the odds run out,
　　and you're feeling mighty low,
Here's a bet that without a doubt,
　　Will make your bankroll grow!"

A good bet is hard to find, but the following one is sure to work if the other party has never seen it before. Take a deck of cards and arrange it so every other card is red from start to finish. Next, cut the deck into two piles. Make sure that the bottom card of one pile is red and the bottom card of the other is black. Riffle shuffle both halves together thoroughly and square up the deck. Now for the fun. State that you will remove cards from the top of the pile two at a time and that you will make the following bet: If the two cards are both the same color you will pay out two dollars; however, if the pair has one red card and one black card you are to receive one dollar.

With such a wager what's the least amount of money you could expect to make every time you ran through the whole deck?

World's Most Incredible "Math Signs" Puzzle

98 + 7 − 6 + 5 − 4 + 3 − 2 − 1 = 100
TOO MANY SIGNS. SOLVE THIS BY USING ONLY
THREE PLUS SIGNS (+)
ONE MINUS SIGN (−)

"Good grief, I think I've been assigned to the wrong class!"

Timmy has indeed been assigned to the wrong class. In the above problem you must write out the digits 9, 8, 7, 6, 5, 4, 3, 2, and 1 in a row and, by inserting plus and minus signs between the digits, come up with a math expression that is equal to 100. Do this using only four signs. Care to sit in on this exam?

World's Most Incredible "Shooting" Puzzle

Squire Pickumoff is shown here regaling the locals with tales of his hunting prowess and boasting of the superiority of his new Black Forest shotgun. Unfortunately for his favorite hunting dog, Rusty, the squire's aim didn't live up to his boasting. Rusty is now half a tail shorter. The squire's plight can be summed up in the following puzzle poem.

> "He _____ to be _____ as a wonderful shot.
>
> He potted his dog and _____ was his lot."

Can you fill in the three missing words? The interesting thing about these words is that they are all made up of the same seven letters.

World's Most Incredible "Drink Stirrer" Puzzler

The fastest waiters down at Wolfgang's Haus of Suds are the Adalbert twins, Ike and Mike. Besides dispensing suds and spuds the boys keep the revellers entertained with a selection of puzzles. The drink stirrer problem below shows an equation using Roman numerals. As stated, the equation is wrong, but if you shift just one of the stirrers to a new position it will be correct. The next round is on you if you fail this test.

World's Most Incredible "Golf" Puzzle

Golf is a very old game indeed. Here we see a young nobleman playing a round of miniature golf in the Borghese Gardens in Rome. The year is 1729 and all his luck has been bad. If, at the end of the front nine, the lad had not lost twice plus half of what he had left after playing eighteen holes, and had he not then lost an additional 80 ducats on the back nine, he would have finished the round with the original 500 ducats he started with. Can you tell how many ducats he did have when he finished the round?

World's Most Incredible "Word Square" Puzzle

L	I	C	E	R	C
C	S	U	I	R	A
S	A	R	T	E	R
E	C	A	R	E	T
T	L	R	U	S	E
M	E	S	E	T	E

One of the oldest and most difficult word puzzles is the word square. Pictured above is a famous six-letter square. To make a problem out of it we have scrambled the letters in each word. To solve it, unscramble the words on the horizontal lines using the helpful hints below. When solved, the same six words appear both horizontally and vertically.

1. What they did with wagons
2. Famous aviator
3. What gold and diamonds are among
4. What artists do
5. Glitter or sparkle
6. That which we all strive for

World's Most Incredible "Vintage Car" Puzzle

Two old car buffs, "Duster" Bigalow and Harlow Highwheeler, are shown here discussing the merits of Harlow's latest acquisition, a reconditioned 1904 Packard Model L.

"That's a grand addition to your collection," said Duster. "Just how many vintage cars do you now have in your collection?"

"Let's see if you can figure it out," replied Harlow. "All but two of my cars are Packards, all but two are Brewster Town cars, and all but two are Duesenbergs. I'll bet you an oil change you can't come up with the answer in five minutes."

How many cars do you think Harlow owns?

World's Most Incredible "Bowling" Puzzle

The other night four old friends, Aaron, Aldwin, Ambrose and Arlen, went down to the Chopping Wood Bowling Alley for a night of kegling. However, since they were all short on funds it was agreed that each player would play each of the other three players only once. How many matches were played that night? You have 30 seconds to strike out on this one.

ANSWERS

Some puzzles have more than one solution. Here are the most common ones.

"Dress" Puzzle (page 6). Since Mrs. Grey is the one who brought the subject up, she can't be wearing grey. She must have on either a white dress or a black dress. The woman who answered her observation was wearing a black dress so Mrs. Grey must then be wearing a white dress. The woman in the black dress can't be Mrs. Black since no one is wearing her own color, and she can't be Mrs. Grey since *she's* wearing white, so she must be Mrs. White. Finally, we come to Mrs. Black, who has to be wearing the grey dress.

"Number" Puzzle (page 7). If you came up with 1 as your answer, you tied with Winthrop. 1,000 plus 1 equals 1001, which is greater than 1,000 times 1, which comes to only 1,000.

"Carpentry" Puzzle (page 8). The following drawing shows how the cuts are made and how the pieces are reassembled:

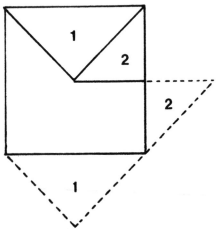

"Billionaire" Puzzle (page 9). The ranking, top to bottom, is: Henry, 6 billion; Everett, 5 billion; Waldo, 4 billion; Alfred, 3 billion; Norbert, 3 billion; Sidney, 2 billion; Winston, 1 billion.

"Tomb" Puzzle (page 10). If you add one match to the first two matches on the table and one match to the last match on the table you will spell out the word "NIX," which means "nothing."

"Real Estate" Puzzle (page 11). Here's the solution Sydney came up with. Is it yours?

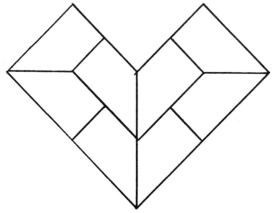

"Automation" Puzzle (page 12). Did you solve it the way our little clown did, or did you end up with a pie in the face?

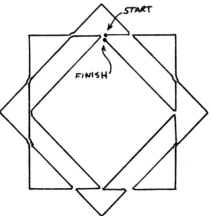

"Match" Puzzle (page 13). This is a very neat puzzle. If you lay out the matches in the form of a triangle you will enclose an area of six square units. However, if you shift the three matches indicated by the broken lines you will drop two square units and be left with a figure that will indeed enclose just four square units.

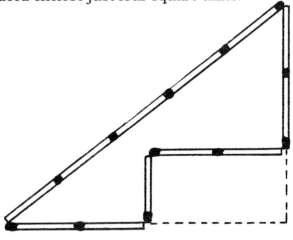

"Checkers" Puzzle (page 14). White to move and win: 32 to 27, 23 to 32, 2 to 7, 11 to 9, 5 to 23, 32 to 27, 23 to 32. The black checker on 28 is blocked from making a move, thereby giving the game to Pop.

"Quotation" Puzzle (page 15). The picture of the clown and the admonition about not being in a rush to solve this problem should have been help enough for you. If you start at the "F" on the lower right-hand side of the frame and read every other letter going clockwise twice around the frame, you'll have the following quotation from Pope's *Essay on Criticism*: "Fools rush in where angels fear to tread."

"Find-the-Items" Puzzle (page 16). The twenty that we came up with are: BAT (BASEBALL), BED, BELL, CABLE (TV), CAT, CLOCK, CLOSET, COAT, COT, DESK, LOCK, SAFE, SOCK, SOFA, STOOL, STOVE, TABLE, TEA, TOOLS, VASE.

"Walking" Puzzle (page 17). Since they saved twenty minutes over the time they usually got back from the station when Barstow would pick her up at 5:00 o'clock, they must have been ten minutes from the station when he met Hattie. At that point he saved going the rest of the way to the station, which would have taken ten minutes. Therefore, he met Hattie at 4:50. Since she arrived at 4:00 o'clock Hattie must have been walking for fifty minutes. It's no wonder she resorted to her basic vocabulary.

"Face" Puzzle (page 18). There are only three complete faces in this picture. If you say the first face is complete then the next one down is overlapped by the one above. If you say the second face from the top is complete then the top face is overlapped. No matter how you work it, there will only be three complete faces in the picture.

"Find-the-Place" Puzzle (page 19). The first city is Utica. "But I can't leave before closing time, Sir!" The second city is Fort Worth. "Is our effort worthy of such a great tune?"

"Archaeology" Puzzle (page 20). The total number of squares is 31. There are 16 small squares; 9 squares composed of 4 smallish squares; 4 still larger squares composed of 9 small squares; 1 diamond square in the center of the tablet; and finally, 1 large square framing the entire tile tablet. You should now know perfection.

"Acronym" Puzzle (page 21).

ETBTFC = Et tu, Brute? Then fall, Caesar. (*Julius Caesar*)

HSTASTIITHATC = How sharper than a serpent's tooth it is to have a thankless child! (*King Lear*)

TBONTBTITQ = To be, or not to be: that is the question. (*Hamlet*)

ARBAONWSAS = A rose by any other name would smell as sweet. (*Romeo and Juliet*)

ORRWATR = O Romeo, Romeo! wherefore art thou Romeo? (*Romeo and Juliet*)

AHAHMKFAH = A horse! a horse! my kingdom for a horse! (*King Richard III*)

"Artist" Puzzle (page 22). The colors are: 1. *blue*nose, 2. *dun*geon, 3. *green*horn, 4. *grey*beard, 5. *hazel*nut, 6. *pink*eye, 7. *lemon*ade, 8. *brown*ie, 9. *red*dogging.

"Toothpick" Puzzle (page 23). Remove the toothpicks from both corners of one side and the toothpick from the middle of the opposite side.

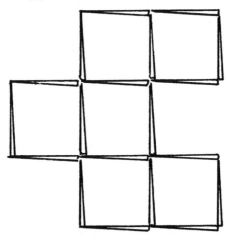

"Riddle" Puzzle (page 24). The answers to the riddles are: 1. A date. 2. Because it's a false hood. 3. When it's adrift. 4. When it is ice.

"Math" Puzzle (page 25).
1. $(2 \times 6) / 3 = (8 \times 8) / 16$
2. $(3 + 9) - 5 = (21 - 7) / 2$
3. $1 + (3 \times 3) + 8 = (2 + 3 + 4) \times 2$

"Treasure" Puzzle (page 26). In this progression each bag contains fewer coins than the preceding bag. Each bag contains a specific fraction of the number of coins in the first bag, which contains 60 coins.

Bag 1 = 60 coins
Bag 2 = 30 coins (½)
Bag 3 = 20 coins (⅓)
Bag 4 = 15 coins (¼)
Bag 5 = 12 coins (⅕)
Bag 6 = 10 coins (⅙)

"Keyboard" Puzzle (page 27). The longest common English word that we know of that can be typed with the second row of keys is *flasks*. Another longer English word is *flagfall*, but this is hardly a common word.

"Medieval" Puzzle (page 28). The complete puzzle should read:

$$
\begin{array}{ccccc}
 & & 1 & 1 & 7 \\
 & & 3 & 1 & 9 \\
\hline
 & 1 & 0 & 5 & 3 \\
 & 1 & 1 & 7 & \\
3 & 5 & 1 & & \\
\hline
3 & 7 & 3 & 2 & 3 \\
\end{array}
$$

"Fusion" Puzzle (page 29). If you make this puzzle up and reassemble it in the shape of a rectangle as shown below, you will note that the line that runs from the upper left-hand corner down to the lower right-hand corner opens up slightly in the middle. We've exaggerated this a bit so that you will see it better. The empty space thus formed is equal in area to that of one of the smaller squares and accounts for the apparent creation of an extra square. Unfortunately, this problem is more a case of confusion than cold fusion.

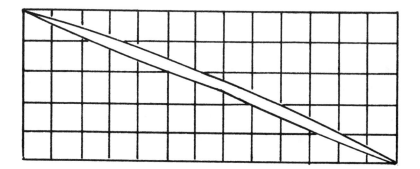

"Domino" Puzzle (page 30).

"Football' Puzzle (page 31). The five answers that we know about are:

1. $99 + \dfrac{9}{9} = 100$ 2. $99\dfrac{9}{9} = 100$ 3. $\dfrac{99}{.99} = 100$

4. $\dfrac{9 \times 9}{.9 \times .9} = 100$ 5. $\left(\dfrac{9}{.9}\right) \times \left(\dfrac{9}{.9}\right) = 100$

"Find-the-Words" Puzzle (page 32). To find the first word remove *six letters*, as called for in the instructions, leaving the word *banana*.

BSAINXLEATNTEARS

To find the second word remove the *six letters sainxl* wherever they appear in the puzzle, which will leave the word *better*.

BSAINXLEATNTEARS

"Butcher" Puzzle (page 33). This is one of those "Gotcha" puzzles. Since a person's weight can't be calculated accurately just by knowing his waist size, the only correct answer to the question "What does a butcher weigh" would have to be "meat."

"Easy 'Z' " Puzzle (page 34). Figure 1 shows where the cuts are made and figure 2 shows how the pieces are reassembled to form a square.

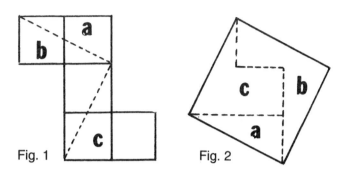

Fig. 1   Fig. 2

"Bloodhound" Puzzle (page 35). When the guards started after Knuckles he was 1½ miles ahead of them. One hour later the guards were 4 miles from the boat while Knuckles was 4½ miles from it. When the guards caught up with Knuckles, half an hour later, they were all 6 miles from the boat. The total capture time was 1½ hours, which means the dog, running at the rate of 12 miles an hour, covered a total distance of 18 miles.

"Substitution" Puzzle (page 36).
$$\frac{219}{3} = 73 \qquad \frac{438}{6} = 73 \qquad \frac{657}{9} = 73$$

"Toy" Puzzle (Page 37). Calvin paid $60.00 for each tractor, $15.00 for each shovel and $5.00 for each truck. The total for lot number three came to $950. The total for lot number four was $80.

"Magic Coins" Puzzle (page 38). Turn over coins 3 and 4, then coins 4 and 5, and finally coins 2 and 3.

"Rectangle" Puzzle (page 39). The first thing to remember is that a square is also a rectangle. With this in mind, let's see where the answer 51 rectangles came from.

Rectangles with one small square:	12
Rectanges with two small squares:	16
Rectangles with three small squares:	8
Rectangles with four small squares:	9
Rectangles with six small squares:	4
Rectangles with eight small squares:	2
Total =	51

"Chicken" Puzzle (page 40). The answer is 24 eggs. It works out that one chicken can lay ⅔ of an egg in one day. Therefore, six chickens can lay four eggs in one day and 24 eggs in six days.

"Alice" Puzzle (page 41). Each of these words can be reduced, one letter at a time, to form new words. Each time you can remove either a first or last letter and be left with a new word. The answers are sometimes different depending on which letter you drop.

1. Brandy, brand, bran, ran, an, a.
2. Pirated, pirate, irate, rate, rat, at, a.
3. Swingers, swinger, swinge, swing, wing, win, in, I.
4. Tramps, ramps, ramp, ram, am, a.
5. Grangers, rangers, range, rang, ran, an, a.

"Weight" Puzzle (page 42).

Box 1 weighs 5½ pounds.
Box 2 weighs 6½ pounds.
Box 3 weighs 7 pounds.
Box 4 weighs 4½ pounds.
Box 5 weighs 3½ pounds.

"Spirit" Puzzle (page 43). The answer is $138 \times 138 = 19,044$

"Trolley Ride" Puzzle (page 44). Since the trolley goes three times as fast as Maynard and Emmeline can walk, they had to spend six hours of the total travel time walking home. Therefore, the other two hours on the trolley will cover 18 miles from Emmeline's home to Olympic Park. The total round trip then is 36 miles.

"Numero Uno" Puzzle (page 45). The two numbers are 11 and 1.1. When added or multiplied together they give a result of 12.1.

"Printing" Puzzle (page 46). Philo will have to purchase twenty-seven pieces of type, for $135, in order to be able to print every month of the year. The letters needed are:

AABCDEEEFGHIJLMNOOPRRSTUUVY
January will need seven letters (JANUARY);
February will need four letters (FEBR);
March will need three letters (MCH);
April will need three letters (PIL);
August will need four letters (GUST);
September will need two letters (EE);
October will need two letters (OO);
November will need one letter (V);
December will need one letter (D).

"Musical Toys" Puzzle (page 47). All told there were 11,376 toys in stock. Cedric received 3,456 toys, Julian 3,600 toys, and Alfred 4,320 toys.

"Addition" Puzzle (page 48).

Charlie's answer is:

1	X	X		1	0	0
3	3	X		3	3	0
5	X	5		5	0	5
X	7	7		0	7	7
X	9	9		0	9	9
1,1	1	1		1,1	1	1

"Square" Puzzle (page 49). The following drawing contains exactly 100 squares and is drawn with only 15 straight lines. There are 40 with squares of one unit; 28 of four units; 18 of nine units; 10 of sixteen units; and four of twenty-five units.

A B C D E F

"Masked Lady" Puzzle (page 50).

12	15	18	5
17	6	11	16
7	20	13	10
14	9	8	19

"Witch" Puzzle (page 51). The statement he made was, "I will be fed to the bats!" If it is true, he will be boiled in oil. If it is false he will be fed to the bats. No matter how you interpret it, you can't work out the correct punishment, so the witch was foiled until another Halloween.

"Suitcase" Puzzle (page 52). The four shapes are all the same although some are mirror images of each other.

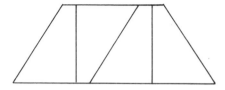

"Scales" Puzzle (page 53). Mrs. O'Toole weighs 135 pounds, the baby weighs 25 pounds, and the dog weighs 10 pounds.

"Counterfeit Coin" Puzzle (page 54). This is one of the most difficult of all counterfeit coin problems. The counterfeit coin could be either heavier or lighter than the other coins. You must find the answer in only 3 weighings. The schematic diagram presented here gives you the answer. The result of all comparisons (in boxes) is based on comparing the top figure(s) to the bottom figure(s). **L** stands for light. **H** stands for heavy.

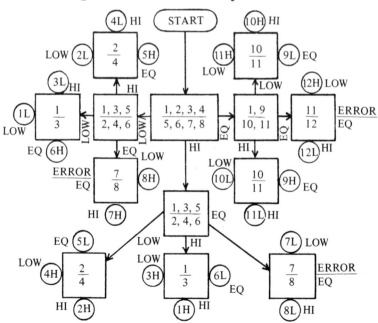

"What" Puzzles (page 55). The answers are: 1. One minds his peas, the other his cues. 2. An upright piano. 3. The figure 6. 4. They're all cabinetmakers. 5. The locomotive.

"Shakspearian" Puzzle (page 56). The plays are:
1. *Coriolanus* (3,6,9,12,15,18,21,24,27,30)
2. *Othello* (25,28,31,34,1,4,7)
3. *Hamlet* (26,29,32,35,2,5)

"Abe Lincoln" Puzzle (page 57). If you check a five-dollar bill you will find that Abe Lincoln is face up on both sides of the bill. On the back of the bill is a small statue of him looking out from the center of the columns on the Lincoln Memorial. Since he is looking out he is clearly face up on this side of the bill too. As long as the bill keeps coming up heads when it is dropped, J. Wellington will win. When it comes up tails he will win again, but no one will bet with him again.

"Card Square" Puzzle (page 58). The three additional card squares are:

3	2	4	6	5	7	9	8	10
4	3	2	7	6	5	10	9	8
2	4	3	5	7	6	8	10	9

The four leftover cards are three aces and a ten. The four squares add up to 9, 15, 18, and 27, respectively.

"Scholar" Puzzle (page 59). The word is *bookkeeper*, and the clue is *accountant*.

"Punctuation" Puzzle (page 60). The following is Alice Flutterheart's rather convoluted writing style:

Melicent, while Fabian had had "had," had had "had had." "Had had" had had a better effect on the teacher.

"Route" Puzzle (page 61). There are exactly 70 different routes Otto could take before he was forced to start over again.

"Guru" Puzzle (page 62). He was talking about the number 1½. After all, ½ is one third of it. What else?

"Sears Hat" Puzzle (page 63). If the hat cost $3.75 more than the fancy cord did, the cord must have cost 25 cents and the hat $4.00. Together, they cost $4.25.

"Bridge" Puzzle (page 64). Deirdre is married to Horace, Imogene is married to Claude, and Erika is married to Selwyn.

"Superstition" Puzzle (page 65). This is a tricky one, and it may have more than one answer. Here's the one we know:

$(3)^3 + (3)^3 + (3)^3 + (3/3)^3 + (3 \times 3) + (3 \times 3) = 100$

or

$27 \quad + \quad 27 \quad + \quad 27 \quad + \quad 1 \quad + \quad 9 \quad + \quad 9 = 100$

"Brick" Puzzle (page 66). Stacks stacked the bricks as shown here. He then reached down through the center of the stack and gripped the bottom brick. Holding on to it, he was then able to lift all five bricks straight up off the ground, thus winning his bet.

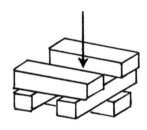

"Knife and Egg" Puzzle (page 67). If you hold the knife tightly and bang the handle down hard on the tabletop all that will happen is that the egg shell will bounce on the knife without the knife penetrating it. What you must do is pretend to strike the table with the knife. However, just before the handle is about to hit the table, let go of the knife just enough for it to strike the table and bounce back up. This bouncing action will cause the end of the knife to penetrate the shell. With a little practice you can do this and have it appear as if you were holding onto the knife throughout the entire proceedings.

"Birthday" Puzzle (page 68). His birthday is on December 31st. In the puzzle picture on the train Mr. Gotrocks is speaking to himself on January 1st. Two days previously, December 30th, he was 54. The next day, December 31st, he was 55. At the end of this new year he will become 56, and next year he will become 57.

"Tree" Puzzle (page 69). The trees are oak, elm, pine, peach, pear, apple, maple, plum, palm, fig, sumac (or sumach), beech, willow, spruce, cedar, larch, and fir.

A	O	W	R	A	S
K	L	I	N	B	D
L	F	P	E	E	A
O	P	A	C	H	G
W	M	L	R	U	I
S	U	E	S	P	F

"Radio" Puzzle (page 70). The answers are: 1. T (tea), 2. N-V (envy), 3. S-X (Essex), 4. X-S (excess), 5. S-A (essay), 6. T-P (teepee), 7. F-E-G (effigy), 8. C-D (seedy), 9. M-T (empty), 10. L (ell), 11. N-M-E (enemy), 12. L-E-G (elegy).

"Doggie" Puzzle (page 71). 1. Dogma, 2. dog days, 3. doge, 4. doggerel, 5. dogwatch, 6. dogleg.

"Mind Reading" Puzzle (page 72). When the mists cleared, Madame Zorrina saw that the word that the gentleman was thinking about was . . . *forty.*

"Indian" Puzzle (page 73). Matches are, of course, made of *love.*

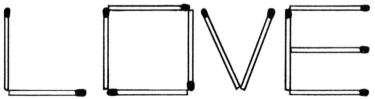

"Typewriter" Puzzle (page 74). 1. Tall tales. 2. Lover come back to me. 3. Small crosses and great ease before marriage; great crosses and little ease after marriage. 4. See both sides of the question. 5. Stranger in paradise. 6. Backward glance. 7. Holy water.

"Sharpshooter" Puzzle (page 75). When Big Nose "hung the hat up" he hung it on the end of his six-shooter. After that the trick worked itself.

"Prohibition" Puzzle (page 76). Here's how Swifty's deliveries went: 1. Sal's received 8 cases—2 more than Hanratty's. 2. Hanratty's received 6 cases—2 more than the Dutchman's Cafe. 3. The Dutchman's Cafe received 4 cases—2 more than Edna's Hide-a-Way. 4. Edna's Hilde-a-Way received 2 cases—6 fewer than Sal's Saloon.

"Beheading" Puzzle (page 77). 1. fox, ox, 2. bark, ark, 3. toil, oil, 4. bore, ore, 5. plane, lane, 6. flute, lute, 7. grow, row.

"Change-the-Word" Puzzle (page 78). With this type of puzzle you're more than likely to come up with one or more different answers. We give you the ones that we are familiar with. (The solution of the puzzle EYE to LID could have been solved with one less move: EYE, LYE, LIE, LID.)
1. *Warm, ward, word, cord, cold.*
2. *More, lore, lose, loss, less.*
3. *Fish, fist, fiat, feat, meat.*
4. *River, liver, liter, later, water.*
5. *Work, worn, warn, earn.*

"Halloween" Puzzle (page 79). The family consisted of two boys and two girls, their mother and father and both their mother's and father's parents (That is, their two grandfathers and two grandmothers.)

"Santa Claus" Puzzle (page 80). The two solutions that we know of are:

24,794	36,156
− 16,452	− 28,693
8,342	7,463

"Subtraction" Puzzle (page 81). I'll let the good Professor give you the answer. "This is somewhat of a quibble. The number 45 is the sum of the digits 1, 2, 3, 4, 5, 6, 7, 8, 9. The puzzle is solved by arranging these digits in reverse order, and subtracting the original series from them, when the remainder will be found to consist of the same digits in a different order, and therefore making the same total, *viz.*, 45."

$$987654321 = 45$$
$$123456789 = 45$$
$$\overline{864197532} = \overline{45}$$

"Airmail" Puzzle (page 82). Wing Walker visited the following eight cities:

1. TAELMBIRO = Baltimore
2. ACOIHGC = Chicago
3. RSBNBATARAAA = Santa Barbara
4. AWTIHIC = Wichita
5. WSLNOEARNE = New Orleans
6. SNGWIOTANH = Washington
7. NLLCADVEE = Cleveland
8. TDYODIGCE = Dodge City

"Computer" Puzzle (page 83). The answer is . . . 301. Do the divisions with pencil and paper to see the remainder.

"Piggy" Puzzle (page 84). Move the two bottom sticks inside the two squares above. You now have a third square inside the other two squares, for a total of three squares.

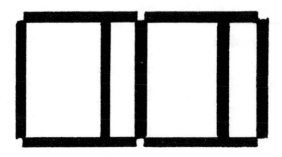

"Word" Puzzle (page 85). The first word is *boldface*, a typesetting term. The second is *feedback*, the information you get in a survey, for example.

"Sawing" Puzzle (page 86). If you came up with 22½ pounds per piece . . . you're wrong. You're not far off, but you're still wrong. Each time Ebenezer cut a section of the beam some of the weight of the beam was lost in the sawdust that fell to the ground. Since an ounce or two would have been lost in the cutting operation, it's impossible to say exactly how much each of the pieces weighed, although they each weighed the same amount. Ebenezer must have had a keen eye when it came to measuring each cut.

"Beer" Puzzle (page 87). In one day Brunhilda drinks:

$$\frac{1}{14} - \frac{1}{20} = \frac{20}{280} - \frac{14}{280} = \frac{6}{280} = \frac{3}{140}$$

Brunhilda drinks $\frac{3}{140}$ of a barrel of beer a day. Divide 140 by 3 and get 46⅔ days, the length of time it used to take Brunhilda to knock off a barrel by herself.

"Pyramid" Puzzle (page 88). The following design will keep him from being inventoried along with the canopic jars.

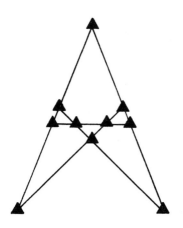

"Movie Musical" Puzzle (page 89). There are seven different piano arrangements that Buzzy could have used. They are:

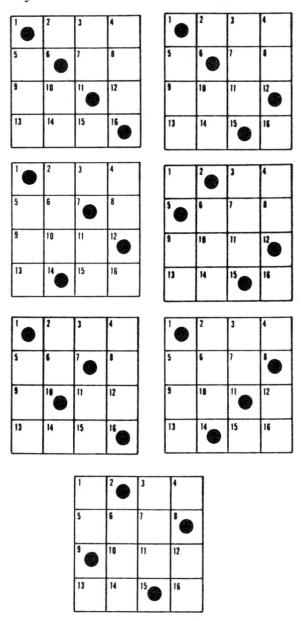

"Stamp" Puzzle (page 90). There are several basic shapes that occur several times:

1. The shape represented by stamps 1,2,3,4 occurs 3 ways.
2. The shape represented by stamps 1,2,5,6 occurs 6 ways.
3. The shape represented by stamps 1,2,3,5 or 1,2,3,7 or 1,5,6,7 or 3,5,6,7 occurs 28 ways.
4. The shape represented by stamps 1,2,3,6 or 2,5,6,7 occurs 14 ways.
5. The shape represented by stamps 1,2,6,7 or 2,3,5,6 or 1,5,6,10 or 2,5,6,9 occurs 14 ways.

All told, there are 65 different ways to tear the four stamps off the sheet.

"Geometry" Puzzle (page 91). The following solution is the one that we know of:

"Baseball" Puzzle (page 92). If you place the three outfielders at three tables and then try placing the three basemen at their tables you will see that there are six possible combinations. Now, if you imagine adding the shortstop, pitcher, and catcher to these various combinations you will see that there are six additional combinations for each. Thus, the total number of different combinations is six times six, or 36. Sometimes the same three players will be at one table but the other two tables will have different players.

"Poker Chip" Puzzle (page 93). Move chips 2 and 3 to squares 9 and 10. Move 5 and 6 to squares 2 and 3. Move 8 and 9 to squares 5 and 6. Move 1 and 2 to squares 8 and 9.

"Sugar" Puzzle (page 94). The Lone Star State would have given Mr. Okito an idea as to the shape of the figure formed by the correct placement of the sugar cubes.

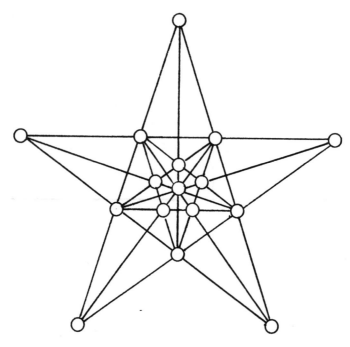

"Betting" Puzzle (page 95). You will always win $26 with this bet. That's right, every pair will contain one red and one black card. Because the bottom card of each pile is a different color when you riffle shuffle the deck together the cards will always fall in an alternating order. Try it and see for yourself. However, you are only allowed one riffle shuffle.

"Math Signs" Puzzle (page 96). The answer to Timmy's heart-stopping puzzle is:

$$98 - 76 + 54 + 3 + 21 = 100$$

"Shooting" Puzzle (page 97). The words are *aspired*, *praised*, and *despair*.

"Drink Stirrer" Puzzle (page 98). One times one equals one.

"Golf" Puzzle (page 99). At the end of 18 holes the young nobleman was left with 120 ducats. Here's how to solve it: First subtract the 80 ducats he lost on the back nine from the 500 he originally started with, leaving 420 ducats.

Next, let

x = half what he had left at the end of the round;

$2x$ = what he had left at the end of the round;

$4x$ = twice what he had left.

Now, add them all together:

$x + 2x + 4x = 420$ ducats;

$7x = 420$ ducats;

$x = 60$ ducats;

$2x = 120$ ducats, the amount he was left with at the end of the round.

"Word Square" Puzzle (page 100).

C	I	R	C	L	E
I	C	A	R	U	S
R	A	R	E	S	T
C	R	E	A	T	E
L	U	S	T	R	E
E	S	T	E	E	M

"Vintage Car" Puzzle (page 101). Harlow owns three cars.

"Bowling" Puzzle (page 102). They played a total of six games. Player A played B, C, and D. Player B played C and D. Player C then played D. At this point, player D had played everyone. The total number of games was 3 + 2 + 1 = 6.

About the Author

Charles Barry Townsend has been writing about puzzles, games, and magic for over 23 years. He is the author of 19 books, including *The World's Best Puzzles, The World's Most Challenging Puzzles, The World's Toughest Puzzles, The World's Most Baffling Puzzles, The World's Hardest Puzzles, The World's Best Magic Tricks, The World's Greatest Puzzles,* and *The World's Most Amazing Puzzles,* all published by Sterling Publishing Company. Mr. Townsend lives in Mill Creek, Washington, where he spends a good deal of his time thinking up ways to confound and entertain readers like you.

Pictured below we see the author and his dog, Jackie, discussing the World's Most Incredible Doggie Puzzle, which appears on page 71, with Santa.

Index

Answer pages are in italics